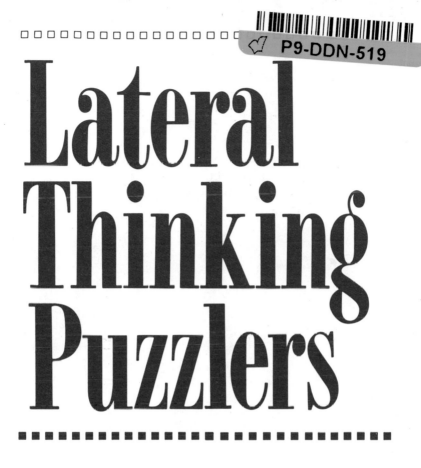

Lateral Thinking Puzzlers

PAUL SLOANE

Illustrated by Myron Miller

Sterling Publishing Co., Inc.   New York

ACKNOWLEDGMENTS

The author acknowledges the inspiration of Martin Gardner, Edward de Bono, Bruno Brookes, and Gyles Brandreth. The puzzle 'The Two Writers' is an idea created by D. StP. Barnard and was originally published in the *Daily Telegraph* in 1978. "The Dream" is the copyright of Times Newspapers and was first published in the *Sunday Times* in 1990.

Edited by Claire Wilson

Library of Congress Cataloging-in-Publication Data

Sloane, Paul, 1950–
    Lateral thinking puzzlers / by Paul Sloane.
        p.   cm.
    ISBN 0-8069-8226-8
    1. Puzzles.   2. Creative thinking.   I. Title.
GV1493.S594   1991
793.73—dc20   90-49158
                                     CIP

First paperback edition published in 1992 by
Sterling Publishing Company, Inc.
387 Park Avenue South, New York, N.Y. 10016
© 1991 by Paul Sloane
Distributed in Canada by Sterling Publishing
% Canadian Manda Group, P.O. Box 920, Station U
Toronto, Ontario, Canada M8Z 5P9
Distributed in Great Britain and Europe by Cassell PLC
Villiers House, 41/47 Strand, London WC2N 5JE, England
Distributed in Australia by Capricorn Link Ltd.
P.O. Box 665, Lane Cove, NSW 2066
Manufactured in the United States of America
All rights reserved

Sterling ISBN 0-8069-8226-8 Trade
       ISBN 0-8069-8227-6 Paper

CONTENTS

Dedicated to Jackie, Katy and Hannah without whose help and inspiration this book would not have been possible.

INTRODUCTION

This book is the result of the many years I spent collecting lateral thinking problems and the happy hours I whiled away trying to figure them out. The reader will doubtless find that some of the puzzles are familiar old faithfuls, but I guarantee that he or she will also find some interesting new ones.

Edward de Bono first coined the phrase "lateral thinking" to refer to a process of thinking that is different from the normal linear, or forward thinking to which we are accustomed. In traditional reasoning, we progress logically from one step to the next. However, in lateral thinking, you must deliberately abandon this process in order to eliminate inhibitions. You then try to solve problems in different, random, or lateral ways.

Most of the problems in this book take the form of situations that at first seem unlikely or illogical. The idea is to work out the set of circumstances that describes the situation. The first section consists of the puzzles, which are split into four categories according to their approximate level of difficulty and a special historical section. The second section consists of leads and clues to give intermediate help with each puzzle. Finally, the last section contains the answers.

Although the reader can work through the book on his or her own, it is much more fun to treat the puzzles as challenges for small groups, either as an after-dinner game or as a lateral thinking exercise. For these events, the best course of action is for one person to act as the quizmaster. He or she, knowing the answer, would then give the question to the group. The leader can then answer questions from the players in one of three ways—yes, no, or irrelevant. The task of the group is to completely solve the problem as fast as it can. This can prove a stimulating, infuriating, and ultimately enjoyable exercise!

If the group gets stuck, then the quizmaster can help by giving some of the leads or clues in the help section.

In asking questions about a situation, you should first test all assumptions. Then make broad attacks on the problem before homing in on promising lines of enquiry. Above all, you should try to think laterally, that is to cast away conventional approaches and to make leaps of the imagination.

THE PUZZLERS

1 Easy Puzzlers

1.1 The Man in the Elevator

For a start, here's one of the oldest and best-known lateral thinking problems. It goes like this:

A man lives on the tenth floor of a building. Every day, he takes the elevator to the first floor to go to work or to go shopping. When he returns, he always takes the elevator to the seventh floor and then walks the remaining flights of stairs to his apartment on the tenth floor. Why does he do this?

1.2 Bombs Away!

One night during the Second World War, an allied bomber was on a mission over Germany. The plane was in perfect condition and everything on it worked properly. When it had reached its target, the pilot ordered the bomb doors opened. They opened. He then ordered the bombs released. They were released. But the bombs did not fall from the plane. Why should this be so?

1.3 The Coal, Carrot, and Scarf

Five pieces of coal, a carrot, and a scarf are lying on the lawn. Nobody put them on the lawn, but there is a perfectly logical reason for their being there. What is it?

1.4 The Two Americans

There were two Americans waiting at the entrance to the British Museum. One of them was the father of the other one's son. How could this be so?

1.5 The Man Who Hanged Himself

Not far from Madrid, there is a large wooden barn. The barn is completely empty except for a dead man hanging from the central rafter. The rope around his neck is ten feet long and his feet are three feet off the ground. The nearest wall is 20 feet away. It is not possible to climb up the walls or along the rafters, yet he hanged himself. How did he manage it?

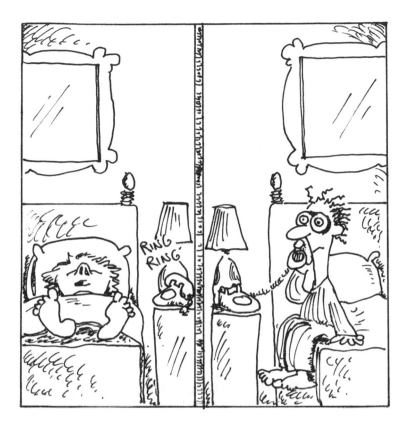

1.6 The Men in the Hotel

Mr. Smith and Mr. Jones are two businessmen who book into the same hotel for the night. They are given adjacent rooms on the third floor. During the night, Mr. Smith sleeps soundly. However, despite being very tired, Mr. Jones cannot fall asleep. He eventually phones Mr. Smith and falls asleep immediately after hanging up. Why should this be so?

1.7 The Silent Cabbie

A London cab driver picked up a lady who was a notorious chatterbox. He did not want to engage in conversation, so he pretended to be deaf and dumb. He pointed to his mouth and ears to indicate that he could neither speak nor hear. After she alighted, he pointed to the meter so that she could see how much she owed. She paid him and walked off. Then she realized that he could not have been a deaf mute. How did she know?

1.8 A Peculiar House

Mrs. Jones wanted a new house. She very much liked to see the sun shining into a room, so she instructed the builders to construct a house of which all four walls face south. After much thought, the builder managed to erect just such a house. How did he do it?

1.9 Death in the Phone Booth

A man is lying dead in a telephone booth. The telephone handset is swinging. Two of the windows are broken. He was not murdered. How did he die?

1.10 The Man in the House

A man entered a house. There was no one else in the house. He walked into a room, stopped, and then slowly raised his hands above his head. After a moment, he turned around, let out a laugh, and left. Why?

1.11 A Chess Piece

Two grandmasters played five games of chess. Each won the same number of games and lost the same number of games. There were no draws in any of the games. How could this be so?

1.12 Happy or Sad

Three women dressed in swimsuits were standing together. Two were sad and one was happy. But the sad women were both smiling and the happy one was crying. Why should that be so?

1.13 The Unseen Walker
. . . .

On a busy Friday afternoon, a man walked several miles across London from Westminister to Knightsbridge without seeing anybody or being seen by anybody. The day was clear and bright. He had perfect eyesight and he looked where he was going. He did not travel by any method of transport other than by foot. London was thronged with people yet not one of them saw him. How?

1.14 The Dream
. . . .

The boss of a storage warehouse had just arrived at work when one of his employees burst into his office. The man explained that while asleep the previous night he had dreamed that one of the stored boxes contained a bomb that would explode at two p.m., causing a terrible fire. The boss was skeptical, but agreed to investigate. After a search, a bomb was found in the area foreseen in the man's dream. The police were called, the bomb defused, and a tragedy averted. Afterwards, the boss thanked the employee sincerely and then fired him.

The sacked man had not planted the bomb, and his prophetic dream had saved the warehouse from destruction. Yet the manager was right to fire him. How could that be so?

1.15 In the Pet Shop
. . . .

A pet shop was advertising puppies for sale. Two men entered the shop. The first put ten dollars on the counter and asked for a puppy. The assistant asked whether he would prefer a poodle, a Labrador, or an Alsatian. He chose the poodle. The second man also put ten dollars on the counter and asked for a puppy. The assistant did not utter a word. He simply gave the man an Alsatian puppy. How did he know that this was what the man wanted?

1.16 The Coffee Drinker

A man in a restaurant complained to the waiter that there was a fly in his cup of coffee. The waiter took the cup away and promised to bring a fresh cup of coffee. He returned a few moments later. The man tasted the coffee and complained that this was his original cup of coffee with the fly removed. He was correct, but how did he know?

1.17 One Step Beyond

A man stood looking through the window on the sixth floor of an office building. Suddenly, he was overcome by an impulse. He opened the window and leapt through it. It was a sheer drop outside the building to the ground. He did not use a parachute or land in water or on any special soft surface. Yet the man was completely unhurt when he landed. How could that be so?

1.18 The Turkish Bath Mystery

Four men met every Thursday lunchtime at the Turkish Baths. Joe, a musician, always brought his personal cassette player so that he could listen to music. Jack, a banker, brought a thermos containing a drink. Jim and John were both lawyers and brought paperback books to read.

One day in the mist-filled room, John was found dead from a deep wound through his heart. The police were called immediately. They questioned all three suspects, but no one said that they had seen anything happen. A thorough search was carried out, but no murder weapon could be found. What happened?

2 Moderate Puzzlers

2.1 Anthony and Cleopatra

Anthony and Cleopatra are lying dead on the floor in an Egyptian villa. Nearby is a broken bowl. There are no marks on their bodies and they were not poisoned. Not a person was in the villa when they died. How did they die?

2.2 Five Men

Five men were proceeding together down a country path. It began to rain. Four of the men quickened their step and began to walk faster. The fifth man made no effort to move any faster. However, he remained dry and the other four got wet. They all arrived at their destination together. How could this be so?

N.B. They relied only on foot power!

2.3 Trouble with Sons I

A woman had two sons who were born in the same hour of the same day in the same year, but they were not twins. How could this be so?

2.4 Trouble with Sons II

A woman sat at her kitchen table with her two sons. She spoke to each of her sons and they replied to her, but the sons never spoke to each other. The boys had not fallen out and did not dislike each other. Although they conversed freely with their mother, they never addressed a word to one another. Why?

2.5 The Two Sisters

One day, two sisters decided to clean out the old shed at the bottom of their garden. When they had finished the cleaning, one of them had a dirty face and the other had a clean face. The sister with the clean face went and washed her face, but the girl with the dirty face did not wash. Why should this be so?

2.6 The Miller's Daughter

Many years ago, there was a poor miller who could not afford to pay the rent on his mill. His grasping old landlord threatened to evict him, his wife, and his daughter. However, the landlord did offer an option. If the miller's beautiful young daughter would marry the old man, then he would forget their debts and let the miller and his wife live in the mill rent-free.

The family met to discuss this proposition. The daughter was horrified at the prospect of marriage to the old man, but she realized that it might be the only hope for her parents. She suggested a compromise. They would draw lots. If the landlord won, she would meet his request and if she won, he would wipe out all debts without her having to marry him. The landlord agreed.

The two stood on a stony path that had many black and white pebbles. The landlord suggested that they put one black pebble and one white one in a bag. She would have to draw a pebble from the bag. If it were black, she must marry him and if it were white she would be free. She reluctantly agreed to this suggestion. He bent down and picked up two pebbles to put in the bag, but she noticed that he had cheated and put in two black pebbles.

She could expose him by showing that there were now two black pebbles in the bag, but he would lose so much face in front of all the people there that he would be very angry and probably evict them. How could she seem to go along with the plan and triumph knowing that there were two black pebbles in the bag?

15

2.7   Water and Wine

There are two glasses on the table, one containing water and the other one wine. They both contain exactly the same amount by volume. If you take a teaspoon of water and mix it into the wine and then take a teaspoonful from the wine glass and mix it with the water, both glasses become contaminated. But which is the more contaminated? Does the water now contain more wine than the wine does water or the other way round?

2.8   The Man in the Painting

A man stands in front of a painting and says the following: "Brothers and sisters have I none. But this man's father is my father's son." How is the man in the painting related to the man who is in front of it?

2.9   The Single Statement

An explorer was captured by a tribe whose chief decided that the man should die. The chief was a very logical man and gave the explorer a choice. The explorer was to make a single statement. If it was true, he would be thrown over a high cliff. If it was false, he would be eaten by lions.

What statement did the clever explorer make that forced the chief to let him go?

2.10   Birthday Blues

The day before yesterday Freda was 17. Next year she will be 20. How can this be so?

2.11   The Four Sheep

Farmer Giles has four sheep. One day, he notices that they are standing in such a way that they are all the same distance away from each other. That is to say, the distance between any two of the four sheep is the same. How can this be so?

2.12 A Geography Question

A ship passed through the Panama Canal from west to east. That is to say, it entered the west end of the Canal and left at the east end. However, immediately after it left the canal, it entered the Pacific Ocean. It did not double back through the canal, nor did it sail backward. How could this be so?

2.13 Family Reunion

At a family reunion, it was found that the following relationships existed between the people present: Father, Mother, Son, Daughter, Uncle, Aunt, Brother, Sister, Cousin, Nephew, Niece. However, there were only four people there. How could this be so?

2.14 Crossing the Desert

Two trucks have to carry the same heavy loads across a desert. One is an older truck with an older driver, Joe, who knows his way to the village that is their destination. The other truck is more modern, but its driver, Jim, does not know the way. They agree that the modern truck will follow the older one. Unfortunately, Jim has forgotten to fill up with fuel. By the time he does this, the first truck is well out of sight. However, it has left very clear tracks in the sand, and Jim follows them.

After some time, the tracks start to become less and less clear. Eventually, they disappear altogether. This surprises Jim, because there is no wind to cover the tracks and his own tracks are still very clear. There is no sign of the other truck, but in due course a bedouin on a camel arrives, and, with his help, Jim gets to the village. There, he meets Joe and discovers the reason why the tracks disappeared. What was it?

2.15 Old Mrs. Jackson

Mr. and Mrs. Jones were young and active people. Their next-door neighbor, Mrs. Jackson, was a 93-year-old invalid. One day, they asked her into their house to do something that neither of them could do. There was no skill that she had that one of them did not have, so why did they need her help?

2.16 Matrimonial Problems

John and David were brothers. John married Jane. David married Diana. The strange thing was, John and Diana shared the same wedding anniversary. David's wedding anniversary was one month before this date and Jane's was one month after it. None of them had ever divorced or remarried. What was going on?

18

2.17 The Man with the Wood

A man had some wood. On Monday, it was in the shape of a cube. On Tuesday, he changed it into the shape of a cylinder, and on Wednesday, he changed it into the shape of a pyramid. He did not cut or carve the wood into these shapes. How did he do it?

2.18 Stuck Tight

A truck became wedged under a low bridge. It could not move forward or back without severely damaging its roof. The truck driver was perplexed until a little girl standing nearby suggested an easy solution. What was it?

2.19 Coming Home

A man walked home after having been out drinking. He walked down the middle of a deserted country road. There were no street lights to illuminate the road and there was no moonlight. He was dressed all in black. Suddenly a car that did not have its headlights on came racing down the road. At the last moment, the driver of the car saw the man and swerved to avoid him. How did he manage to see him?

2.20 A Riddle

For a little light relief, we will now have an old riddle. What is it that gets wetter as it dries?

2.21 Another Riddle

What is it that the man who makes it does not need; the man who buys it does not use himself, and the person who uses it does so without knowing?

2.22 The Horse Dyed

A man went buffalo hunting. He rode a beautiful white stallion and carried a powerful rifle to shoot his prey. Unfortunately, the buffalo could see the white horse approaching and ran off long before he could shoot. The hunter hit on the plan of dying the horse brown so as to camouflage it. He painted a brown dye on the horse and went hunting again. The camouflage worked, but he was even less successful with his hunting than before. Why?

2.23 Push That Car

A man pushing his car stopped outside a hotel. As soon as he got there, he knew he was bankrupt. Why?

2.24 The Unrequested Kiss

In the middle of the day, a young woman approached a man in the street. Without either of them saying a word,

she gave him a long kiss on the lips. She had never seen him before and she did not know who he was. She did not find him attractive and she was not rewarded for her actions. So why did she kiss him?

2.25 The Two Golfers
. . . .
Archie and Ben were professional golfers and keen rivals. One day during a game, they had each scored 30 when Ben hit a bad shot. Archie immediately added 10 to his own score. Archie then hit a good shot and he had won the game. Why?

3 Historical Puzzlers

3.1 Sew What?

In 1685, it was decided that a portrait should be painted of the Duke of Monmouth. However, a needle and thread were required before the artist could begin his work. There was nothing wrong with the Duke's clothes, so why were the needle and thread needed?

3.2 The Grateful Prisoner

In 1902 in the French West Indies Mr. Cyparis was in prison awaiting trial for drunkenness. He was detained longer than he expected, was neglected, and was left without food and water. Yet when he was released, he was grateful to have been in prison. Why should that be so?

3.3 Ben Jonson

Ben Jonson was a great English poet and playwright who lived from 1572 until 1637. Why was he buried in a sitting position?

3.4 Lord Strathallen

Lord Strathallen was an important Scottish nobleman who was used to getting what he wanted. One day in 1746, he ordered some food and drink even though he was neither hungry nor thirsty. What he wanted was not available and he was offered whiskey and oatcake instead. He was glad to quickly consume a little of each. Why?

3.5 A Remarkable Journey

In 1930, two men drove from New York to Los Angeles in a Ford motor car. The journey of 3,340 miles took 18 days.

This wasn't the first, the fastest, or the slowest journey

of its kind. They drove on normal roads. The car was not remarkable and the two men were normal. But because of this journey, these two men hold a world record that endures to this day. What is it?

3.6 The Two Writers

George and Evelyn never met but they carried on writing until late in life. It has been said that Evelyn loved George, but she was in any event too old for him. George married in 1880. He converted to Catholicism in 1930. During World War II, he served with the Royal Marines and the Royal Horse Guards. Partly in recognition of this, Evelyn's subsequent writings analyzed the character of World War II and the struggle between good and evil.

Evelyn died in 1966 near Taunton in Somerset. She had achieved notoriety for her unconventional views and lifestyle. Her first full-length novel had been published in 1859. She is buried in Highgate Cemetery. He died at the age of 62 having published his autobiography in 1964. He lived one year longer than she did. How could this be so?

3.7 World War I

At the beginning of the first World War, the uniform of the British soldiers included a brown cloth cap. They were not provided with metal helmets.

As the war went on, the army authorities and the War Office became alarmed at the high proportion of men suffering head injuries. They therefore decided to replace the cloth headgear with metal helmets. From then on, all soldiers wore the metal helmets. However, the War Office was amazed to discover that the incidence of head injuries then increased. It can be assumed that the intensity of fighting was the same before and after this change. So why should the recorded number of head injuries per battalion increase when men wore metal helmets rather than cloth caps?

3.8 King George IV

King George IV was born in 1763. He was king of England from 1820 until his death in 1830. He was not a great king, but he did start a new trend in footwear. His boots were different from everybody else's. The innovation concerning his boots was copied and it is commonplace today, but at the time was very unusual. What was it?

3.9 Walk This Way

Johann Hurlinger, an Austrian, set a world record by walking the 871 miles from Vienna to Paris in 55 days. He averaged only 1.5 miles per hour and he did it in 1900, yet the record stands today. What is so special about it?

4 Difficult Puzzlers

4.1 Death in a Field

A man is lying dead in a field. Next to him is an unopened package. There is no other creature in the field. How did he die?

4.2 Death in Rome

Mr. Jones is reading his daily newspaper. He reads an article with the following headline: "Woman dies in holiday accident." It goes on to say, "Mrs. Rigby-Brown, while on holiday with her husband in Rome, fell to her death from the balcony of her seventh-floor room."

Mr. Jones turns to his wife and says "That was not an accident. It was murder." He had never met either of the Rigby-Browns, so how could he know it was murder?

4.3 Woman on the Bridge I

During the second World War, there was a footbridge over a ravine between Germany and Switzerland. It was guarded by a German sentry. His orders were to shoot anyone trying to escape over the bridge and to turn back anyone who did not have a signed authorization to cross. The sentry was on the German side of the bridge. He sat in a sentry post and he came out every three minutes to survey the bridge.

There was a woman who desperately needed to escape from Germany to Switzerland. She could not possibly get a pass. She knew that she could sneak past the sentry while he was in the sentry post, but it would take between five and six minutes to cross the bridge. There was no place to hide on or under the bridge, so the guard would be easily able to shoot her if he saw her on the bridge escaping to Switzerland. How did she escape across that bridge?

4.4 Woman on the Bridge II

In South America, a woman was being chased by a gang of bandits. She had escaped with two solid gold balls, and the bandits wanted to kill her and take the balls. She came to a wooden bridge over a deep ravine. The bridge was 100 feet long. There was a notice on the bridge that said "Maximum weight on this bridge 112 pounds." Strangely enough, this notice was 100% accurate—the bridge would break if it carried more than 112 pounds. She weighed 100 pounds and each of the two balls weighed 10 pounds. There was no time to leave one ball behind and come back for it later. And yet she managed to escape across the bridge to safety with both the balls. How could this be so?

4.5 Trouble with Sons, Again!

This is more of a probability teaser than a lateral thinking problem, but it can prove amusing.

Mrs. Jones has two children. At least one is a boy. What are the chances that both are boys?

Mrs. Brown has two children. The younger is a boy. What are the chances that both are boys?

4.6 Silence on the Train

A man boarded a train and sat in a carriage. The only other person in the carriage was a woman who was sitting opposite him. After a little while, she took from her bag a pencil and paper and passed it to the man. He wrote on the piece of paper and gave it back to her. At the next stop, she got off the train and threw the piece of paper away.

They had never met before. Their meeting on the train was by chance and not arranged. They did not speak to each other.

Can you determine the story behind this sequence of events?

4.7 The Lonely Man

A man lived alone in a house for two months. Nobody came to visit him and he never went out. At the end of that time, he became deranged. One night he put out the fire, turned off the lights, and walked out of the house. He was never seen or heard of again. His actions in leaving that house resulted in the deaths of 90 people. Why was that?

4.8 The Distant Image

A man was in a room. It was ten feet square and ten feet high with solid walls, ceiling, and floor. There were no windows and the door was close fitting and closed. It was a dark night and no light entered the room from outside.

There was a light on in the room. Apart from the light, there was no other electrical or powered object in the room. The interesting thing is this—although the room was only ten feet across, the man could see something 40 feet away. How could that be?

4.9   Coins of the Realm

Why are 1988 pennies worth more than 1983 pennies?

4.10   Baby Has Lots

What is it that a baby has more of than an adult?

4.11   The Hotel Detective

A hotel detective was walking along the corridor of a large hotel one day. Suddenly, he heard a woman's voice cry out "For God's sake, don't shoot me John!" Then there was a shot. He ran to the room from where the shot came and burst in. In one corner of the room, lay a woman who had been shot through the heart. In the middle of the floor was the gun that had been used to shoot her. On the other side of the room stood a postman, a lawyer, and an accountant. The detective looked at them for a moment and then went up to the postman, grabbed him, and said "I am arresting you for the murder of that woman."

It was, in fact, the postman who had murdered the woman, but how did the hotel detective know? Never before had he seen any of the people in the room.

4.12   Faster Than the Speed of Sound

What was the first man-made object to travel faster than the speed of sound?

The speed of sound is about 1100 feet per second (340 metres per second). Concorde travels faster than the speed of sound. But the answer to this question is an object created a long time before Concorde.

4.13 Concorde

A businessman had an important business meeting that led him to fly by Concorde from London to New York. When he left home in the morning, his wife drove him to the airport and accompanied him to the check-in. She then waved good-bye as he went through to Passport Control and the Departure Lounge. She did some shopping at the airport shops and returned to the car at which time she saw the Concorde take off on time.

His flight on Concorde from London to New York was of course a direct flight. When he reached New York, he went directly through Immigration and Customs. He had no baggage to collect as he only took a briefcase for his short trip. He went through to the arrivals hall and there waiting to greet him was his wife! It was only that morning that she had seen him off. She had not flown nor taken a boat so how could she be there to meet him?

4.14 Asphyxiation

A woman was found gassed in her bedroom. The gas fireplace had been left on. The windows and door were locked from the inside. She had been seen entering the room by her sister. It looked to the police as though she had accidentally put the gas on and forgotten to light it, so they put it down as an accident. In fact, her husband had murdered her. How?

4.15 The Slow Mover

Although the people who come to see it think it moves forward, it actually moves backwards. It started about seven miles from where it is today and is moving now much slower than in the past. Previously, it travelled as much as five feet a year, but now it's travelling less than half that distance. Despite its slow speed, most of the people who have tried to ride along on it have perished in the attempt. What is it?

4.16 Dinner for Three

. . . .

An ancient Arabic puzzle goes like this: A hunter met two shepherds, one of whom had three loaves and the other, five loaves. All the loaves were the same size. The three men agreed to share the eight loaves equally between them. After they had eaten, the hunter gave the shepherds eight bronze coins as payment for his meal. How should the two shepherds fairly divide this money?

4.17 A Theological Puzzle

. . . .

Years ago, a boy was brought before his headmaster because he had not learned his scripture lesson. After a long lecture, the headmaster offered to let him off his beating if he could show that he knew anything about God that the headmaster did not know. The boy then asked a question that completely stumped the man: "What is it that you can see and I can see but that God can never see?"

The headmaster thought there could be no answer, but when he heard the boy's response, he had to concede that it was true. So the clever boy escaped his punishment. What was the answer?

4.18 It's a Knock-out!

A policeman was called because a man was found lying unconscious outside a shop. As soon as the man came around, he was arrested. He was not a known criminal and had not been engaged in any kind of fight or dispute before losing consciousness. Why did the policeman arrest him?

4.19 The Frustrated Policemen

The police in Venezuela have been trying to arrest a notorious criminal for some time. They know where he lives. On several occasions, they have obtained a warrant for his arrest and have gone to his house. However, as soon as they enter the house, he locks himself in his bedroom. The police then go away frustrated. Why should that be so?

4.20 Neighbors

Ali, Ben, and Cyril were born in 1309, 1310 and 1311 in the same district in old Jerusalem. They grew up and lived their whole lives in this same area. Each lived to be over 60 and each had a full and active life. However, the three men never saw each other. Why should that be so?

4.21 The Fatal Fare

A man got into a taxi and told the driver his destination. After that, they did not say a word. On the way, the taxi driver stopped the taxi at a lonely spot and beckoned the man to get out. The driver then picked up a stone and dealt his passenger a heavy blow to the head, killing him. He then drove off.

The taxi driver was not a criminal. He had never met the passenger before nor did he recognize his face or voice. He did not rob the man. Why did he kill him?

4.22 One Clock

In the days before watches were invented, clocks were valuable items. There was a man who had one clock in his house. It kept good time, but one day he found that it had stopped. He had no idea what the correct time was. He walked to the next valley to visit his friend who had a clock showing the right time. He spent a little while chatting with his friend then he walked home. He did not know the exact length of the journey before he started. How did he manage to set his one clock correctly on his return?

5 Fiendish Puzzlers

5.1 The Man in the Bar I

For its brevity, its simplicity, and its difficulty, this problem has some claims to be the best lateral thinking problem ever.

A man walked into a bar and asked the barman for a glass of water. They had never met before. The barman pulled a gun from under the counter and pointed it at the man. The man said 'Thank-you' and walked out. Why should that be so?

5.2 The Man in the Bar II

A man walked into a bar and asked for a drink. The man behind the bar pulled out a gun and shot the man. Why should that be so?

5.3 The Man in the Bar III

A man who wanted a drink walked into a bar. Before he could say a word, he was knocked unconscious. Why?

5.4 Another Man in a Bar

Two brothers were having a drink in a bar. Suddenly, one of the brothers got into a heated argument with the barman. He pulled a knife and, despite his brother's attempts to stop him, stabbed the barman in the chest.

At his trial, he was found guilty of assault with a deadly weapon and grievous bodily harm. At the end of the trial, the judge said "You have been found guilty of a vicious crime. However, I have no choice but to set you free."

Why should this be so?

5.5   The Deadly Block of Wood

A man lies dead inside a trailer. He has shot himself. Close by him is a block of wood. It is a plain piece of wood about two feet long by one inch wide (61cm by 2cm). The wood carries no writing or other markings and yet, it is fair to say that the sight of this piece of wood on this day caused the man to commit suicide. Why should this be so?

5.6   The Two Barbers

A traveller came to a small town. He had never visited it before, he knew no one there, and he knew nothing about the town or its inhabitants.

He needed a haircut. There happened to be two barber shops close to each other on the main thoroughfare—the only barber shops in town. The man studied each of them with care. One shop was very neat and tidy. Everything about it was smart. The barber was sweeping away the last traces of hair from the floor while waiting for his next customer.

The other barber's shop was very untidy. Everything looked rather run down and ramshackle. The scruffy-looking barber within was lolling on a chair waiting for his next customer.

Both shops charged the same amount for a haircut. After careful consideration, the traveller decided to go to the scruffy barber for his haircut. Why?

34

5.7   The Mongolian Postal Service.

The Mongolian Postal Service has a strict rule stating that items sent through the post must not be more than 1 metre long. Longer items must be sent by private carriers, and they are notorious for their expense, inefficiency, and high rate of loss of goods.

Boris was desperate to send his valuable and ancient flute safely through the post. Unfortunately, it was 1.4 metres long and could not be disassembled as it was one long, hollow piece of ebony. Eventually, he hit on a way to send it through the Mongolian Postal Service. What did Boris do?

5.8   Heaven

A man died and went to Heaven. There were thousands of other people there. They were all naked and everyone looked as they did at the age of 21.

He looked around to see if there was anyone he recognized. Suddenly, he saw a couple, and he knew that they were Adam and Eve. How did he know?

5.9   Fool's Gold

You must choose between two cylinders. They are identical in size and appearance. Each is painted green. However, one is solid and made of a non-magnetic alloy. The other is hollow and made of gold. They both have solid ends. They both weigh the same, measure the same, and have the same density. You are not allowed to scratch through the paint. How can you simply tell which cylinder is made of gold?

5.10   The Man in the Bar, Again!

A man walked into a bar and asked for a drink. The barman had never met the man before but without saying a word he pulled out a gun and shot him dead. Why?

5.11 The Plane Hijacker

A few years ago in the USA, a young man hijacked a passenger flight at gunpoint. He ordered the pilot to fly to a different airport and radioed his demands to the airport authorities. In return for the safe release of the plane and hostages, he asked for 100,000 dollars in a bag and two parachutes. When the plane landed, he was given the bag of money and the two parachutes. He then instructed the pilot to take off again and to fly at a fairly low altitude towards their original destination. When they were over a deserted part of the country, he strapped on one of the parachutes and, clutching the bag of money, leapt from the plane. The second parachute was not used. .

He was never found. The task of the police is to find that hijacker. Your task is different. You have to answer one question. Why did he ask for two parachutes if we assume that he only ever intended to use one?

5.12 Wealth Tax

The governing body of the state of Lateralia was extremely concerned about the uneven distribution of wealth in the country. They thought it unfair that the richest man in the country should have so very much more than his poorer compatriots. They therefore instituted a wealth tax decreeing that each year the wealthiest man in the country had to give away his money by doubling the wealth of every other citizen, starting with the poorest and working up to the second wealthiest person if possible. This decree was carried out, and the richest man gave away his money by doubling the wealth of all other citizens. However, the governing body was shocked to find that this action had made no difference to the overall distribution of wealth nor to the relative wealth of the poorest and richest citizens. How could this be so?

5.13 Death on the Train

A man stepped out of a speeding train to his death. He had been on his own in the compartment, and all that was found there was a very large handkerchief. If he had made the journey by any means other than train, he would almost certainly not have decided to commit suicide. Why did he take his life?

5.14 The Amorous Commuter

John Jones lives in Maidenhead. He has one girlfriend in Reading and another in Slough. He has no car and therefore takes the train whenever he goes to see them.

Trains stopping in Maidenhead can go either east or west. If they are westbound they will go to Reading. If they are eastbound, they will go to Slough. There are an equal number of trains going in each direction.

John likes his two girlfriends equally. Because he finds it hard to choose between them, he decides that when he goes to the station, he will take the first arriving train, regardless of whether it is going east or west. After he has done this for a month, he finds that he has visited the girl in Slough 11 times as often as he visited the girl in Reading. Assuming that he arrived at Maidenhead station at random times, why should the poor girl in Reading have received so little of his attention?

5.15 Short Roads

There are four main towns in Lateralia. We will call them A, B, C and D. They lie at the corners of a ten-mile square. In order to improve communications between the towns, the Lateralian Department of Transport decided to build a new road linking all four towns together. Because they had very little money, it was decided that the new road system should be as short as possible and still allow access from any one town to any other. The engineers came up with the three designs shown below. Number one uses 40 miles of road, number two uses 30 miles of road, and number three uses 28.3 miles of road. The designers naturally recommended plan number three because it employed the smallest road area and, therefore, cost the least. However, when they submitted their plan to the Minister of Finance, he accused them of extravagance and quickly pointed out a better design that required even less total road surface. What was his superior solution?

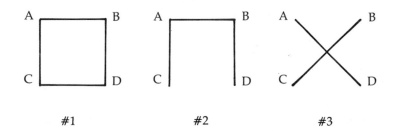

#1   #2   #3

5.16 The Hunter and the Bear

There is a well-known puzzle that goes like this:
There was a hunter who started out from his camp one morning. He walked one mile due south and then saw a bear. He followed it eastward for exactly one mile, at which point he shot it. He then dragged it northward for one mile to the same camp that he had started from. What color was the bear?

5.17 The Arm of the Postal Service

One day a man received a parcel in the post. Inside, he found a human left arm. He examined it carefully and then repacked it and sent it on to another man. The second man also examined the arm. He then took it out to the woods and buried it. Why should they have done these things?

5.18 A Weighty Problem I

A shopkeeper wants to be able to dispense sugar in whole pounds ranging from one pound up to 40 pounds. He has a standard, equal-arm balance weigh scale. Being of an extremely economical outlook, he wants to use the least possible number of weights to enable him to weigh any number of pounds between 1 and 40. How many weights does he need and what are they?

5.19 A Weighty Problem II

This problem is more than weighty, it is devilish.
You have an equal-arm balance scale and twelve solid balls. You are told that one of the balls has a different weight from all the others, but you do not know whether it is lighter or heavier. You can weigh the balls against each other in the scale balance. Can you find the odd ball and tell if it is lighter or heavier in only three weighings?

THE CLUES

1 Easy Puzzlers

1.1 The Man in the Elevator

Q: Is there anything that he does between the seventh and tenth floors other than climb stairs?
A: No.

Q: If he had someone else with him, would they both get out at the seventh floor and walk up to the tenth floor?
A: No.

Q: If he lived on the sixth floor, would he go up to the sixth floor in the elevator?
A: Yes.

Q: If he lived in a different block of apartments in a different country but still on the 10th floor, would he still get out on the 7th floor when going up?
A: Most probably yes.

1.2 Bombs Away!

Q: Would the fact that the bombs did not fall surprise any of the crew?
A: No.

Q: If that same plane was parked on the runway and the bomb doors were opened and the bombs released, would they fall?
A: Yes.

Q: Was the manner in which the plane was flying the cause of the bombs not dropping?
A: Yes.

1.3 The Coal, Carrot, and Scarf

Q: Does the time of year matter?
A: Yes.

Q: Were the coal, carrot, and scarf brought out to the garden by human beings?
A: Yes.

Q: Were they used for some entertainment purpose?
A: Yes.

1.4 The Two Americans

This one is based on a familiar theme. You either get it quickly or not at all. It does not lend itself to a long line of intelligent questioning. It boils down to the simple question—how can two people have the same son?

1.5 The Man Who Hanged Himself

Q: Was there anybody else involved before, during, or after his suicide?
A: No.

Q: Did he stand on something in order to reach the rafter?
A: Yes.

Q: Has that something now gone?
A: Yes.

Q: Did someone take it away?
A: No.

1.6 The Men in the Hotel

Q: Was there something happening in Mr. Smith's room that was preventing Mr. Jones from sleeping?
A: Yes.

Q: Was it a noise?
A: Yes.

Q: Did they speak for long on the phone?
A: No.

1.7 The Silent Cabbie

This little problem is best solved by thinking clearly about how a passenger uses a taxi. What communications take place between passenger and cabbie?

1.8 A Peculiar House

This house had only four walls and they all faced south. Think about the shape of the house, then think about where it might be located.

1.9 Death in the Phone Booth

Q: Was he talking to someone when he died?
A: Yes.

Q: Was his death an accident?
A: Yes.

Q: Did anything external hit the phone booth?
A: No.

Q:Did he break the phone booth windows?
A: Yes.

Clue: There was a fishing rod outside the phone booth.

1.10 The Man in the House

Q: Was he frightened when he raised his hands?
A: Yes.

Q: Was it his house?
A: No.

Q: Had he heard a sound that made him raise his hands?
A: Yes.

Q: Did he laugh because he was surprised and relieved?
A: Yes.

1.11 A Chess Piece

This is the kind of problem that depends on the reader or listener making the wrong initial assumptions. Test all the assumptions with questions like the following:

Q: Were they playing normal chess?
A: Yes.

Q: In chess, if one player wins then the other loses?
A: Yes, always.

Q: So when one grandmaster won a game, the other grandmaster lost it?
A: No.

Q: Was there anybody else involved?
A: Yes.

1.12 Happy or Sad

Q: Were they on the beach or at a swimming pool?
A: No.

Q: Is it relevant that they were wearing swimsuits?
A: Yes.

Q: Were they beautiful, shapely women?
A: Yes.

Q: Was the happy one crying because she was happy?
A: Yes.

Q: Were the sad ones smiling because they were sad?
A: No.

1.13 The Unseen Walker

Q: If he walked into this room now, would we see him and he see us?
A: Yes.

Q: Did he wear anything special?
A: Yes. *Clue:* It was a miner's helmet.

Q: Did he walk along normal roads?
A: No.

1.14 The Dream

Q: Was the man sacked because he had had anything to do with planting the bomb?
A: No.

Q: Had the man genuinely dreamed about the bomb?
A: Yes.

Q: Did the boss have a grudge of some kind against the man?
A: No.

Q: Were the man's particular responsibilities relevant?
A: Yes.

44

1.15 In the Pet Shop

Q: Was this the last puppy?
A: No, there were plenty of puppies of all three breeds.

Q: Were any of the three men known to each other.
A: No.

Q: Did the second man gesture in any way that he wanted the Alsatian?
A: No.

Q: Had the customer ever been in the shop before?
A: No.
Clue: Every dog has his price.

1.16 The Coffee Drinker

Q: Was there something about the cup itself that identified it?
A: No.

Q: Was the fly still in the cup?
A: No.

Q: Could the man have known it was the same cup if he had not tasted it?
A: No.

1.17 One Step Beyond

Q: Was he holding a rope?
A: No.

Q: Did he have special powers or could anyone have done this?
A: Anyone could have done this.

Q: Did he fall from six floors and land on the ground outside the building?
A: No.

Q: Did he jump through the window?
A: Yes.

45

1.18 The Turkish Bath Mystery

Q: Was John murdered by one of his three companions?
A: Yes.

Q: Was he stabbed by one of them?
A: Yes.

Q: Did the murderer bring the weapon into the baths with him?
A: Yes.

Q: Could the police have found the weapon if they had searched harder?
A: No.

2 Moderate Puzzlers

2.1 Anthony and Cleopatra

This is an old one. It can prove a little difficult if you have not heard it before.

The most fruitful lines of questioning are those that try to establish the exact cause and circumstances of death. To cut a long story short, it can be said that their deaths followed the accidental breaking of the bowl. The bowl had contained water. They died from lack of oxygen.

2.2 Five Men

Q: Did the man who stayed dry carry any kind of umbrella or other covering?
A: No.

Q: Did he walk?
A: No.

2.3 Trouble with Sons I

This is one of those problems that can appear totally mystifying and impossible to explain. However, you will kick yourself when you hear the answer.

Suffice it to say that the two boys are brothers, born of the same mother and father on the same day of the same year at the same place. But they were not twins. What else could they be?

2.4 Trouble with Sons II

Q: Were all three people physically normal with full faculties of speech, hearing, sight, etc.?
A: Yes.

Q: Had they ever spoken directly to each other?
A: No.

Q: Would they like to speak to each other?
A: Yes.

Q: Is there any physical barrier that prevents them conversing?
A: No.

Q: Had they grown up together?
A: No.

2.5 The Two Sisters

This is another problem that involves making the wrong assumptions. In this case, you need to question the assumptions and motivations of the two girls.

Q: Did the girl who washed want to clean her face?
A: Yes.

Q: Did she think that her face was dirty?
A: Yes.

Q: So the girl who did not wash thought that her face was already clean?
A: Yes.

2.6 The Miller's Daughter

You have to think of a way whereby she could use the fact that she knows she will draw a black pebble to give a result that will indicate a white pebble. If that is too obscure just remember that a double negative is a positive, that should help.

2.7 Water and Wine

This is quite a celebrated little problem. It can be solved mathematically or by the application of some common sense and lateral thinking.

The important point to bear in mind is that, after the two transfers, each glass contains the same volume that it started with and the same volume as the other glass.

2.8 The Man in the Painting

This is a simple little riddle but it often causes consternation. If you get into a muddle with it then just divide the sentence into three parts:

Brothers and Sisters have I none,
But this man's father
Is my Father's Son.

Now work backwards from the last statement.

2.9 The Single Statement

The explorer must make a statement that is both true and false at the same time. Better still, it should be a statement that means that any action the chief takes would place him in the position of having acted illogically.

Can you construct a statement about the way the explorer will die that is neither true nor false?

2.10 Birthday Blues

Freda has to have three birthdays between the day before yesterday and the end of next year. So the birthday has to fall around the turn of the year. You should be able to get it from there.

2.11 The Four Sheep

Start by defining how three sheep can be equidistant from each other—it's easy isn't it?

Your mind should then jump from a triangle to a square. But if you find that a square cannot produce a solution then, you need to start thinking laterally, i.e. along different lines entirely!

2.12 A Geography Question

Q: Did the ship enter the canal from the Caribbean Sea?
A: Yes.

Q: It then sailed from the west end of the canal to the east end?
A: Yes.

Q: And it then entered the Pacific Ocean?
A: Yes.

Q: Was this a special ship in some way?
A: No.

Q: Does every ship do this?
A. Yes.

2.13 Family Reunion

This is not a trick question in any sense. All the relationships are present between the people there. Do not start with any false assumptions. For example, husband and wife are not mentioned!

Try leaving the brother and sister relationship to last and start with the aunt, uncle, cousin, etc.

2.14 Crossing the Desert

This is a conventional lateral thinking problem with a familiar underlying theme. Concentrate the questions on

49

why the tracks of the old vehicle (only) should grow gradually fainter and disappear.

2.15 Old Mrs. Jackson

Q: Did Mrs. Jackson perform any physical action for the Joneses?
A: Yes.

Q: Was it something that they could do or learn to do for themselves?
A: No.

Q: Would Mrs. Jackson have been able to perform the same service for some other couple?
A: Yes.

2.16 Matrimonial Problems

Each sentence in itself is true. The key is the second sentence. These questions should help make things a little clearer:

Q: Is John married to Jane?
A: No.

Q: Is David married to Diana?
A: No.

Q: Is John married to Diana?
A: Yes.

Q: Is David married to Jane?
A: No.

2.17 The Man with the Wood

Q: Did he have it in blocks that he rearranged?
A: No.

Q: Did he use fire or heat to mould it?
A: No.

Q: Was it wood from a tree?
A: Yes.

Q: Did changing the wood's shape require a special skill?
A: No.

2.18 Stuck Tight

Q: Were the bridge and truck normal?
A: Yes.

Q: Could the road be lowered or the bridge raised?
A: No.

Q: Was the girl's idea easy to implement, without any special equipment?
A: Yes.

2.19 Coming Home

Q: Was the man carrying a torch or any other illumination?
A: No.

Q: Was there any starlight or lightning?
A: No.

Q: Did the driver see the man?
A: Yes.

Q: Could anyone have seen him?
A: Yes.

2.20 A Riddle

It is difficult to give any clues on this neat riddle other than to advise you to consider the question actively, not passively!

2.21 Another Riddle

It could also be said that nobody wants it, but everybody needs it!

2.22 The Horse Dyed

Q: Did the brown dye make the horse slower or less able to chase buffalo?
A: No.

Q: Was it solely the dye that caused the deterioration in his hunting chances or was there some other factor (such as fewer buffalo or worse light)?
A: It was solely the dye.

Q: Did the dye make the horse harder to see?
A: Yes.

2.23 Push That Car

Q: Did he have to push the car?
A: Yes.

Q: Could the car ever be driven?
A: No.

Q: Was the hotel on a famous road?
A: Yes.

Q: Was he bankrupt because he had to pay money to the hotel owner?
A: Yes.

2.24 The Unrequested Kiss

Q: Did she expect to kiss someone on this day?
A: No.

Q: Was there a rational reason for her behaviour?
A: Yes.

Q: Was he expecting a kiss?
A: No.

Q: Was there anything unusual about him?
A: Yes.

Q: Did she do it to help him?
A: Yes.

2.25 The Two Golfers

Clues should not be needed on this one as you have all the information you require to work out the answer, even if you know nothing about golf or its scoring!

3 Historical Puzzlers

3.1 Sew What?

Q: Were the needle and thread needed for the canvas?
A: No.

Q: Was the artist a normal portrait artist?
A: Yes.

Q: Was there something wrong with the Duke of Monmouth?
A: Yes.

Q: Was he alive?
A: No.

3.2 The Grateful Prisoner

Q: Did he meet someone or learn something in prison?
A: No.

Q: Was he better off when he left prison than when he entered it?
A: No.

Q: Was he cured of some disease or illness?
A: No.

Q: Is his offense relevant?
A: No.

Q: Did he enjoy being in prison?
A: No.

Q: Did he avoid something by being in prison?
A: Yes.

3.3 Ben Jonson

Q: Had he asked to be buried in a sitting position?
A: No.

Q: Was it usual for people to be buried like that?
A: No. Extremely unusual.

Q: Did it have something to do with his profession?
A: Yes.

Q: Was he buried in a normal church graveyard?
A: No.

3.4 Lord Strathallen

Q: Did he need the food and drink for some medical condition?
A: No.

Q: Did the whiskey and oatcake meet a real need that he had?
A: Yes.

Q: What did he ask for?
A: Wine and bread.

Q: Was his request urgent?
A: Yes.

3.5 A Remarkable Journey

An important point in the description is that they hold a world record. It is not just a record for going from New York to Los Angeles. The distance and manner of their journey are what count.

It is a remarkable record. It does not involve silly aspects of the car or the men. If in doubt, think laterally!

3.6 The Two Writers

This is really a literary quiz disguised as a lateral thinking problem. If you need some clues then try the following.

George wrote *Silas Marner*. Evelyn wrote *Brideshead Revisited* in 1945, some 86 years after she had written *Adam Bede*.

3.7 World War I

Q: Did the men wear the helmets?
A: Yes.

Q: When they wore the helmets, did the incidence of head injuries increase?
A: Yes.

Q: And yet helmets were retained?

A: Yes.

Q: Were they beneficial?
A: Yes.

3.8 King George IV

What was new about King George IV's footwear had nothing to do with buckles, laces, tongues, heels, soles, color, or material. It was much more fundamental.

3.9 Walk This Way

Q: Did he walk unaided all the way?
A: Yes.

Q: Was he physically handicapped or abnormal in any way?
A: No.

Q: Would it be an easy record to beat?
A: No.

Q: Did he walk on stilts or on any special footwear, or did he carry anything?
A: No.

Q: Were his feet very sore when he finished?
A: No.

4 Difficult Puzzlers

4.1 Death in a Field

Q: Was his death an accident?
A: Yes.

Q: Did he die in the field, in the spot where he lies?
A: Yes.

Q: Was anyone else present in or around the field at the time?
A: No.

Q. If he had been able to open the packet would that have saved him?
A: Yes.

Q: Did he know he was going to die as he entered the field?
A: Yes.

4.2 Death in Rome

Q: Had Mr. Jones ever met either of the Rigby-Browns?
A: No.

Q: Was he right in saying it was murder?
A: Yes.

Q: Was Mr. Rigby-Brown the murderer?
A: Yes.

Q: Had Mr. Jones ever communicated in any way with Mrs. Rigby-Brown?
A: No.

Q: Had Mr. Jones, in his professional capacity, provided some service to Mr. Rigby-Brown?
A: Yes.

Q: Did he deduce from this service and the newspaper article that Mrs. Rigby-Brown had been murdered?
A: Yes.

4.3 Woman on the Bridge I

Q: Did she escape by running over the bridge or hiding on it?
A: No.

Q: Did she escape by tricking the guard in some way?
A: Yes.

Q: Did the guard follow his orders?
A: Yes.

4.4 Woman on the Bridge II

Q: Did she roll the balls over the bridge?
A: No.

Q: Did she throw them to the other side?
A: No.

Q: Did she take them with her as she crossed the bridge?
A: Yes.

Q: Yet the weight on the bridge never exceeded 112 pounds?
A: Correct.

Q: Did she use some special skill?
A: Yes.

4.5 Trouble with Sons, Again!

The answers to the two questions are, of course, different. Try writing down all the possible combinations of boys and girls that can constitute two children. Then work out which of these combinations are applicable in the cases of Mrs. Jones and Mrs. Brown.

4.6 Silence on the Train

This requires some thorough questioning. Here are some useful questions and one or two clues:

Q: Did they recognize each other in any way?
A: No.

Q: Did the man make any movements or gestures?
A: Yes. *Clue:* with his mouth.

Q: Was the man remarkable in any way?
A: Yes. *Clue:* he was a famous author.

Q: Was the woman remarkable in any way?
A: Yes. *Clue:* she was deaf and mute.

4.7 The Lonely Man

Q: Is what he did after leaving the house relevant?
A: No.

Q: Could he have left the house earlier?
A: Yes.

Q: Was it an ordinary sort of a house?
A: No.

Q: Did he perform some function or duty within the house?
A: Yes.

Q: Was the cessation of this function or duty the cause of the deaths of the 90 people?
A: Yes.

Q: Were they involved in some form of travel when they died?
A: Yes.

4.8 The Distant Image

Q: Was there anything else in the room other than the man and the light?
A: Yes.

Q: Were the other thing(s) in the room necessary to the sighting of something 40 feet away?
A: Yes.

Q: Did this man have special skills or powers?
A: No.

Q: Would anyone there have been able to see the thing 40 feet away?

A: Yes.

4.9 Coins of the Realm

Q: Are the 1988 pennies in better condition than the 1983 pennies?
A: No.

Q: Are the 1988 coins rarer than the 1983 coins?
A: No.

Q: Were pennies minted in 1988 and 1983?
A: Yes (but irrelevant!).

4.10 Baby Has Lots

Q: Is the answer something abstract, such as innocence or expectations?
A: No. The answer is something physical that a baby has more of than an adult.

Q: Does the number that a baby has reduce as he or she gets older?
A: Yes.

Q: Does everybody have them and need them?
A: Yes.

Q: Are they part of the body?
A: Yes.

Clue: A baby has about 350 of them and an adult about 206.

4.11 The Hotel Detective

Q: Was the profession of each of the three suspects immediately apparent?
A: No.

Q: Was each wearing normal working clothes?
A: Yes.

Q: Were they wearing name badges or other identifiers?
A: No.

Q: Was it something to do with the position or use of the gun?
A: No.

Q: Was it a brilliant or difficult piece of detective work?
A: No.

Q: Would it have been obvious to most people who the murderer was?
A: Yes.

4.12 Faster Than the Speed of Sound

Q: Does this object make a loud noise as it breaks the speed barrier?
A: Yes.

Q: Is it in use today?
A: Yes.

Q: Is it possible for a man to throw something faster than the speed of sound?
A: No.

Q: Was it normally used as a weapon?
A: No.

Q: Is it easy to get it to break the sound barrier or does it require great strength or skill?
A: Fairly easy for most adults.

4.13 Concorde

This is another problem that repays the questioning of all assumptions made.

Q: Did his wife travel (other than from home to the airport and back again)?
A: No.

Q: Was she in New York to meet him?
A: Yes.

Q: Was she in London to see him off?
A: No.

Q: Did someone else see him off from London?
A: No.

4.14 Asphyxiation

Q: Did anyone other than the woman enter the room?
A: No.

Q: Did she die from breathing gas?
A: Yes.

Q: Had she lit the oven?
A: Yes.

Q: Was the oven faulty in any way?
A: No.

4.15 The Slow Mover

Q: Is it a living thing?
A: No.

Q: Are there many examples of this type of phenomenon?
A: Yes.

Q: Do people come to see it because it is a spectacular sight?
A: Yes.

4.16 Dinner for Three

This is a very straightforward puzzle with no tricks or catches. However, the right answer is not three coins to the shepherd who had three loaves and five coins to the shepherd who had five loaves. That would not be fair!

4.17 A Theological Puzzle

For the purposes of this problem, it is assumed that there is only one God and that God is the supreme being, all knowing and all seeing.

4.18 It's a Knock-out!

Q: Did he suffer from some medical condition or physical disability?
A: No.

Q: Did someone else knock him out?
A: No.

Q: Was he knocked out by a blow to the head?
A: Yes.

Q: Was there anything lying near him?
A: Yes. *Clue:* It was a brick.

4.19 The Frustrated Policemen

Q: Could they arrest him if he stayed in the kitchen or hallway?
A: Yes.

Q: Could they arrest him if his bedroom door was unlocked?
A: No.

Q: Could they arrest him in the street?
A: Yes.

Q: Is the layout of the house the important factor?
A: Yes.

Q: Is there something that physically prevents people from entering his bedroom?
A: No.

4.20 Neighbors

Q: Was there some physical barrier that kept them apart?
A: No.

Q: Were they blind?
A: No.

Q: Was it possible for them to meet?
A: No.

Q: Were they of different religions?
A: Yes.

4.21 The Fatal Fare

Q: Did the taxi driver deliberately murder his passenger?
A: Yes.

Q: Was the murdered man a criminal, a spy, or a relative of the driver?
A: No.

Q: Was it a case of mistaken identity?
A: No.

Q: Did either of them have any kind of illness or disability?
A: No.

Q: Was the taxi driver paid for killing the man?
A: No.

Q: Was the time of day important?
A: Yes.

Q: Was the destination important?
A: Yes.

4.22 One Clock

Q: Did he have any kind of radio, television, or other way of knowing the time?
A: No. This was a long time before the invention of any such things.

Q: Did he use the sun or any other external source of information?
A: No.

Q: Did he use his clock at home in the process of determining the correct time?
A: Yes.

Q: Did he set his clock before he left?
A: Yes.

5 Fiendish Puzzlers

5.1 The Man in the Bar I

Q: Was the barman expecting some kind of message or messenger?
A: No.

Q: Was the man expecting the barman to pull a gun?
A: No.

Q: When the man said 'Thank-you,' did he mean that he was grateful?
A: Yes.

Q: Was the barman normal?
A: Yes.

Q: Was the man normal?
A: No. *Clue:* he had an ailment.

5.2 The Man in the Bar II

Q: Did the two men know each other?
A: No, they were complete strangers.

Q: Was the man behind the bar expecting someone?
A: No.

Q: Was there something unusual or threatening about the man who entered the bar?
A: No.

Q: Did the man who entered the bar really want a drink or did he have some other purpose in mind?
A: Yes, he wanted to drink.

Q: Did the man behind the bar mean to kill him?
A: Yes.

Q: Were either of the men criminals?
A: Yes.

Q: Was the man behind the bar the regular barman?
A: No.

5.3 The Man in the Bar III

No clues on this one. You should be an expert on bars by now!

5.4 Another Man in a Bar

Q: Was the brother really guilty of the crimes?
A: Yes.

Q: Were the brothers identical twins?
A: No.

Q: Was it a case of mistaken identity?
A: No.

Q: Was he physically normal?
A: No.

Q: Did the judge choose to not send him to prison because of his brother?
A: Yes.

5.5 The Deadly Block of Wood

Q: Was the man normal?
A: No. *Clue:* If you find his abnormality you are close to solving the problem.

Q: Did his job depend on his abnormality?
A: Yes. *Clue:* he worked in a circus.

Q: Did he use the wood in relation to his work?
A: Yes.

Q: Had the piece of wood been altered?
A: Yes.

Q: Did he commit suicide because he thought his ability to do his job had been affected?
A: Yes.

5.6 The Two Barbers

Q: Was the man making a considered and rational choice in going to the scruffy barber?
A: Yes.

Q: Was his choice governed solely by the desire to get a good haircut?
A: Yes.

Q: Did he make the right decision?
A: Yes.

Q: Had he seen examples of each barber's work?
A: Yes.

5.7 The Mongolian Postal Service

Q: Did he break or bend the flute in any way?
A: No.

Q: Did Boris send it through the Mongolian Postal Service?
A: Yes.

Q: Did he send it in a container that met the rules of not being longer than one metre?
A: Yes.

Q: Do the Mongolian Postal Service officials measure items correctly with a tape measure along each side?
A: Yes.

5.8 Heaven

Q: Was there some physical difference that distinguished them from all others?
A: Yes.

Q: Would it be immediately apparent to any observer?
A: Yes.

Q: Was it related to the fact that they were the first two humans?
A: Yes.

5.9 Fool's Gold

Q: Can the difference between the two cylinders be determined by their physical appearance?
A: No.

Q: Does the solution to this problem involve carrying out some physical test or experiment?
A: Yes.

Q: Is it simple to perform?
A: Yes.

Q: Does it involve weighing the bars or immersing them in liquid?
A: No.

5.10 The Man in the Bar, Again!

Q: Did the barman know or recognize the man?
A: No.

Q: Did the barman think he recognized the man?
A: Yes.

Q: Did the barman deliberately shoot the man?
A: Yes.

Q: Was his motive revenge?
A: Yes.

Q: Was the barman pleased that he had shot the man?
A: At first yes, but later not.

5.11 The Plane Hijacker

Q: Did the man change his mind during the course of the hijack?
A: No.

Q: So he always intended to leap out of the plane on his own?
A: Yes.

Q: Did he carefully choose one parachute in preference to the other?
A: No.

Q: Did he ask for two parachutes in order to deceive the airport authorities?
A: Yes.

Q: Did he do this to protect himself?
A: Yes.

5.12 Wealth Tax

Q: Did the richest man give away all his money?
A: No.

Q: Did he double the wealth of every other citizen?
A: Yes.

Q: Does it matter how many people there are in Lateralia?
A: No.

Q: Did the pattern of distribution of wealth change?
A: No.

Q: Did the ownership of the wealth change?
A: Yes.

Clue: This wealth tax operation could be carried out every year with a new richest citizen giving away his wealth and still it would make no difference to the overall distribution of wealth in Lateralia.

5.13 Death on the Train

Q: Did the man feel suicidal when he boarded the train?
A: No.

Q: Did something happen on the train to cause him to take his life?
A: Yes.

Q: Was anyone else involved?
A: No.

Q: Was the man in good health?
A: No. *Clue:* he had been recently discharged from hospital.

Q: Had he been wearing the large handkerchief?
A: Yes.

Q: Did he commit suicide because he mistakenly thought he had not been cured?
A: Yes.

5.14 The Amorous Commuter

Q: Does he always take the first train to arrive?
A: Yes.

Q: Does he take 11 times as many trains to Slough as he does to Reading?
A: Yes.

Q: In the course of the day, are there the same number of trains from Maidenhead to Reading as from Maidenhead to Slough?
A: Yes.

Q: Does the answer have anything to do with the timing of the trains?
A: Yes.

5.15 Short Roads

It is hard to believe that a solution exists that requires less road than number 3. After all, the diagonals represent the shortest distance between A and C and between B and D. However, the Minister of Finance was correct. There is a solution which links all four towns with less total road. There are no tricks or corny catches involved.

5.16 The Hunter and the Bear

Obviously, if you go one mile south then one east then one north, you finish approximately one mile west of where you started. The reason it is approximately rather

71

than exactly one mile is because you are on a great sphere—the Earth.

If you analyze the problem in terms of the sphere, then it quickly becomes apparent that at the North Pole you can go one mile south, one east, and one north and return to your starting place. Thus, the bear was a polar bear and therefore white. That was the original puzzle. But some bright spark worked out that the North Pole is not the only geographical solution.

Think about the problem again.

5.17 The Arm of the Postal Service.

Q: Did each of the two men have only one arm?
A: Yes.

Q: Did the man who sent the parcel have only one arm?
A: Yes.

Q: Did the sender amputate his own arm before sending it through the post?
A: Yes.

Q: Did he do this willingly?
A: Yes.

Q: Had all three been present when the first two had lost their arms?
A: Yes.

Q: Was it in the form of an accident?
A: No.

5.18 A Weighty Problem I

Believe it or not, it is possible to weigh any amount between 1 and 40 pounds with just four weights. This assumes that you can put the weights on either side of the balance. If you can put the weights in one pan only (because the other is reserved solely for sugar), then you need all of six weights. But with those six, you can weigh any amount of sugar from 1 to 63 pounds. Now you need to apply straightforward mathematical reasoning to iden tify which weights are needed in each case.

5.19 A Weighty Problem II

This is a very tough problem, but it is solvable with a determined approach. Here are some clues to help you on your way: (1) Every weighing must be designed to yield the maximum amount of information. Therefore, it must be able to offer three possible outcomes—to weigh down to the left or to the right or to balance. (2) If you know that a group of three balls contains the dud ball and you know whether it is heavier or lighter, then you can identify which one it is by weighing any one of the three against any other. (3) Starting with five against five gives you big problems if they do not balance. Similarly, three against three leads to trouble if the first weighing gives a balance. (4) If the scales do not balance, then you know that any balls not on the scales must be true and you can use some or all of those to help in the next weighing.

THE ANSWERS

1 Easy Puzzlers

1.1 The Man in the Elevator

The man is a dwarf. He can reach the button in the elevator for the first floor, but he cannot reach the button for the tenth floor. The seventh floor button is the highest he can reach.

1.2 Bombs Away!

The bomber was flying upside-down!

1.3 The Coal, Carrot, and Scarf

They were used by children who made a snowman. The snow has now melted.

1.4 The Two Americans

They were husband and wife.

1.5 The Man Who Hanged Himself

He climbed on a block of ice, which has since melted.

1.6 The Men in the Hotel

Mr. Jones could not sleep because Mr. Smith was snoring. His phone call awoke Mr. Smith and stopped him snoring long enough for Mr. Jones to get to sleep.

1.7 The Silent Cabbie

He must have heard her initial instructions or he would not have known where to take her.

1.8 A Peculiar House

The builder built the house at the North Pole!

1.9 Death in the Phone Booth

He was describing to a friend the size of a fish that got away. In his enthusiasm, he put his hands through the windows, thereby accidentally slitting his wrists.

1.10 The Man in the House

The man was a burglar intent on robbing the house. When he reached the library, he heard a harsh voice say 'Hands up!' When he looked around, he saw a parrot in a cage.

1.11 A Chess Piece

Who said that they were playing each other?

1.12 Happy or Sad

It was the final of the Miss World Beauty Contest. The winner always cries. The disappointed runners-up smile because everyone is watching them and they are expected to look happy and radiant.

1.13 The Unseen Walker

He walked through the sewers.

1.14 The Dream

The sacked employee was the warehouse night watchman. He should have been awake all night on his security duties. Having a dream proved that he was asleep on the job. For this, he was fired.

1.15 In the Pet Shop

There was a price list on the wall. It showed poodle puppies at eight dollars, Labradors at nine dollars, and Alsatians at 10 dollars. The first man put a ten dollar bill on the counter, so he could have wanted any of the three breeds. The second man put down one five dollar bill and five one dollar bills. The assistant correctly deduced that the second man wanted the Alsatian.

1.16 The Coffee Drinker

He had sweetened the original cup of coffee with sugar. He therefore knew when he tasted the coffee that it was the same cup.

1.17 One Step Beyond

He started off outside the window and leapt into the building. Why was he outside? He could either have been on the ledge contemplating suicide or he could have been the window cleaner. Take your pick.

1.18 The Turkish Bath Mystery

John was murdered by Jack, who brought an ice dagger into the Turkish Baths in his thermos flask. The dagger melted away after the murder leaving no clue.

2 Moderate Puzzlers

2.1 Anthony and Cleopatra

Anthony and Cleopatra were goldfish. They died when their bowl was knocked over by a rather clumsy guard dog.

2.2 Five Men

The four men were carrying the fifth man, who was in his coffin.

2.3 Trouble with Sons I

They were two of a set of triplets!

2.4 Trouble with Sons II

The mother was a Russian who was widowed during the war and who had fled to the West, leaving her first son behind with his aunt and uncle. She settled in France, married a Frenchman, and had a second son. When her first son visited her for the first time, there was a tearful reunion around the kitchen table. However, neither half-brother could speak the other's language, so they could converse only through their mother.

2.5 The Two Sisters

When they had finished the cleaning, they had no mirror to look at, so each girl looked at her sister. The girl with the clean face saw that her sister was dirty and assumed that she would be dirty, so she washed. Her sister made the reverse assumption.

2.6 The Miller's Daughter

Her best course of action is to take a stone from the bag and immediately drop it on the path. She can then say, "We can work out the color of the stone I selected by looking at the one that is left. If that is black, I must have selected the white stone."

2.7 Water and Wine

They are both equally contaminated. The water contains exactly as much wine as the wine contains water. The most elegant proof for this celebrated little puzzle is as follows: It does not matter how many transfers are made between the glasses or whether the contents are stirred. Provided that the volumes in the two glasses are equal, then any water not in the water glass must be in the wine, there is nowhere else it can be. The wine that it has replaced must be in the water glass. The water glass therefore contains as much wine as the wine contains water.

2.8 The Man in the Painting

It is the man's son in the painting. 'My father's son' must be the man himself (since he had no brothers or sisters). Therefore, 'this man's father is my father's son' becomes 'this man's father is me'. So, the man in the picture is his son.

2.9 The Single Statement

The explorer made the statement, "I will be eaten by lions." Now, if the chief does feed him to the lions, his statement will have been true, so he should have been thrown off the cliff. But if he is thrown off the cliff, his statement will have been false. The chief had to admit that the only fair course of action was to let the explorer go free.

2.10 Birthday Blues

The statement was made on January the first. Freda's birthday is on December 31st. She was 17 the day before yesterday. She was 18 yesterday. She will be 19 this year and 20 next year.

2.11 The Four Sheep

The sheep are standing on the four corner points of an equal-sided pyramid. Or to put it another way, three are on the points of an equilateral triangle and the other is on a mound of earth in the centre.

2.12 A Geography Question

Remarkable as it may seem, the west end of the Panama Canal is in the Caribbean and the east end in the Pacific. The Isthmus snakes around at that point and the canal runs from north-west (the Caribbean) to south-east (the Pacific). If you still do not believe it, then look it up in a large scale atlas.

2.13 Family Reunion

There was a brother and sister. The brother's son was there and so was the sister's daughter. From this, it follows that the son and daughter were cousins, and all the other relationships are quite straightforward.

2.14 Crossing the Desert

The two trucks were carrying ice. The older truck was less well insulated that the new one. Its ice therefore melted, making the truck lighter. Its tracks therefore faded.

2.15 Old Mrs. Jackson

Old Mrs. Jackson acted as a witness to a document that both the Joneses signed.

2.16 Matrimonial Problems

John and David were both clergymen. David married John to Diana. That is why they share the same anniversary. John married Jane to her husband. On a separate occasion, John married David to his wife.

2.17 The Man with the Wood

The wood was sawdust. He poured it into a square box to make the cube shape, a bucket to make the cylinder, and then into a pyramid-shaped box to make the pyramid.

2.18 Stuck Tight

The little girl suggested that the driver let some air out of the truck's tires. He let out enough to lower the truck by the small amount required to let it pass under the bridge.

2.19 Coming Home

This puzzle depends on the reader making the false assumption that the man was coming home at night. He was returning home in bright sunlight, so anyone could have seen him.

2.20 A Riddle

The answer is a towel.

2.21 Another Riddle

The answer is a coffin.

2.22 The Horse Dyed

Although the dye made the horse harder to see, it also made it much easier to smell. The buffalo caught the scent of the dye from a long distance and made their escape.

2.23 Push That Car

He was playing Monopoly.

2.24 The Unrequested Kiss

She saved the man by giving him the kiss of life, i.e. mouth-to-mouth resuscitation.

2.25 The Two Golfers

They were playing tennis. At 30-all Ben hit a shot out. Archie then served an ace to win the game and match.

3 Historical Puzzlers

3.1 Sew What?

James, Duke of Monmouth, was beheaded on 15 July 1685 after the defeat of his forces at the battle of Sedgemoor, which ended his challenge to the throne of King James II. After his execution, it was belatedly decided that a portrait should be painted. The head was sewn back onto the body, which was dressed so that the artist could begin his work.

3.2 The Grateful Prisoner

Monsieur M. Cyparis was the sole survivor, out of 30,000 people, of the volcanic eruption of Mont Pelee, which destroyed St. Pierre, capital of Martinique in the West Indies on May 8th, 1902. He had been locked in a strong underground jail cell. All the other people in this once-prosperous town were killed by lava, fire, or poisonous gases.

3.3 Ben Jonson

Ben Jonson, being second only to Shakespeare in his eminence as a poet at that time, was buried in the Poets' Corner in Westminster Abbey. The plot that was allocated to him was so small that he had to be buried in a sitting position in order to fit in it.

3.4 Lord Strathallen

Lord Strathallen was mortally wounded during the battle of Culloden Moor on April 16th, 1746, when the Scots under Bonnie Prince Charlie were defeated by the Duke of Cumberland to end the "Forty-five" rebellion. Lord Strathallen was a Catholic and asked for the Holy Eucharist before he died. The priest could find no bread and wine, so he consecrated oatcake and whiskey instead.

3.5 A Remarkable Journey

They hold the world record for the longest journey driven in reverse. Charles Creighton and James Hargis drove their Ford Model A in reverse all the way from New York to Los Angeles between 26 July and 13 August, 1930. They then drove back to New York again in reverse!

3.6 The Two Writers

The woman was George Eliot, the authoress who was born Mary Ann Evans in 1819 and who took her pen name in order to promote her literary career. She died in 1880, the same year that she married John Cross.

Evelyn Waugh was born in 1903 and he died in 1966.

3.7 World War I

The number of recorded head injuries increased, but the number of deaths decreased. Previously, if a soldier had been hit on the head by a piece of shrapnel, it would have pierced his cap and probably killed him. This would have been recorded as a death, not a head injury. After helmets were issued it was more likely that a fragment of shrapnel would cause an injury rather than death. Thus, the incidence of head injuries increased, while the incidence of deaths decreased.

3.8 King George IV

He had a right boot and a left boot! Until that time, all shoes or boots were made to be worn on either foot.

3.9 Walk This Way

He walked all the way on his hands, and thereby set the world duration record for walking on hands.

4 Difficult Puzzlers

4.1 Death in a Field

The man had jumped from a plane, but his parachute had failed to open. It was the unopened package by his side.

4.2 Death in Rome

Mr. Jones was a travel agent. He had recently supplied by post two plane tickets for a Mr. Rigby-Brown. The two tickets were for Rome, but the one for Mr. Rigby-Brown had been ordered as a return ticket. Mrs. Rigby-Brown's ticket had been one way only.

4.3 Woman on the Bridge I

The woman waited until the sentry went into his hut. She then sneaked onto the bridge and walked towards the Swiss border. She walked for nearly three minutes, then she turned around and started to walk back towards Germany. The guard came out and saw her. When she reached him he saw that she had no authority to enter Germany, and he therefore ordered her to go back—to Switzerland!

4.4 Woman on the Bridge II

She juggled the balls as she went over the bridge.

4.5 Trouble with Sons, Again!

For two children, there are only four possible combinations:

	Older	Younger
A	Boy	Boy
B	Boy	Girl
C	Girl	Boy
D	Girl	Girl

Each of these combinations is equally likely (i.e. there is a one in four chance that any two-child family will have one of the above combinations).

For Mrs. Jones, the possibilities are narrowed down to A B or C and of these, only A means that both are boys. Therefore, the chance that both her children are boys is one in three.

For Mrs. Brown, A and C are the only possibilities. There is thus a one in two chance that both her children are boys.

4.6 Silence on the Train

The man was a moderately well-known author. He sat in the carriage and started to chew gum. The woman was deaf and mute and thought he might be speaking to her. She gave him pen and paper on which to write his message. He, being rather vain, thought she had recognized him as a celebrity and wanted his autograph. He signed the paper. His signature meant nothing to her, so she threw the piece of paper away as soon as she left the train.

4.7 The Lonely Man

He was a lighthouse keeper, and the house in which he lived was a lighthouse on a remote outcrop of rock. When he left the place and turned the lights off, the warning to shipping was removed. A shipwreck occurred resulting in the deaths of 90 people.

4.8 The Distant Image

What he could see 40 feet away was the reflection of his hand. There were mirrors on opposite sides of the room. The man held his hand up and slightly to the side of him. He could see its image reflected many times in the mirror in front of him. The first reflection is 20 feet away, the second is 40 feet away, an so on.

4.9 Coins of the Realm

Why are 20 pennies worth more than 15 pennies? Because there are five more of them! The same is true for 1988 pennies and 1983 pennies. The trouble is caused because the brain automatically sees these numbers as dates.

4.10 Baby Has Lots

A baby is born with some 350 separate bones. As the baby grows, some of these bones join together so that in maturity the same person has only some 206 bones.

4.11 The Hotel Detective

The lawyer and the accountant were women. The postman was therefore the only person who could have been called John.

4.12 Faster Than the Speed of Sound

The first man-made object to travel faster than the speed of sound was the tip of a whip. The characteristic noise of the crack of a whip is the result of the tip breaking the sound barrier.

4.13 Concorde

He lived in New York. His wife saw him off from New York in the morning and greeted him on his return in the evening.

4.14 Asphyxiation

The woman lit the oven and then fell asleep on the bed. Her husband simply turned off the main gas supply into the house and then turned it on again a few moments later. This caused the fire to go out. The gas then filled the room and asphyxiated the unfortunate woman.

4.15 The Slow Mover

The answer is Niagara Falls. It is estimated that the Falls started about seven miles further downstream and have cut their way through the rock. They have therefore moved upstream at a rate of several feet a year ever since.

4.16 Dinner for Three

The shepherd who had three loaves should get one coin and the shepherd who had five loaves should get seven coins.

If there were eight loaves and three men, each man ate two and two-thirds loaves. So the first shepherd gave the hunter one-third of a loaf and the second shepherd gave the hunter two and one-third loaves. The shepherd who gave one-third of a loaf should get one coin and the one who gave seven-thirds of a loaf should get seven coins.

4.17 A Theological Puzzle

The answer was 'an equal.' Other possible answers include a parent or a superior being. However, an equal is the most elegant response.

4.18 It's a Knock-out!

He had been trying to break the shop window in order to rob the shop. He threw a brick at the window but, unfortunately for him, the window was made of reinforced glass. The brick rebounded and knocked him out!

4.19 The Frustrated Policemen

His house is built on the border between Venezuela and Colombia. Although his front door and kitchen are in Venezuela, his bedroom lies in Colombian territory. The Venezuelan police have no jurisdiction in Colombia, so they cannot arrest him as long as he stays in his bedroom.

4.20 Neighbors

Ali was a Muslim, Ben a Jew, and Cyril was Christian. Ali was born in 1309 of the Muslim calendar. The starting point for the Muslim calendar is the emigration of Muhammad from Mecca to Medina in AD 622. Consequently, the Muslim year 1309 equates to 1930 A.D. Similarly, Ben's birthdate falls under the Jewish calendar, which started in 3761 B.C. So Ben was born over 3,000 years before Cyril, who in turn was born 619 years before Ali.

4.21 The Fatal Fare

The customer gave as his destination the taxi driver's home address. The driver had known for some time that his wife had a lover who visited her in the afternoons. He deduced that this was his wife's lover, and therefore murdered him.

4.22 One Clock

He wound his clock and set it at some particular time before he left. He noted the exact time of his arrival at and departure from his friend's house. He noted the time showing on his clock when he returned. He walked at the same pace on the two journeys. The elapsed time on his clock is the duration of the two journeys plus the length of his visit to his friend. Knowing the time he spent with his friend, he subtracts this from the elapsed time on his clock and divides the result by two in order to calculate the duration of the journey. He adds this to the exact time he left his friend's house in order to set his clock at the correct time. For example, assume he set his clock at 12, arrived at his friend's at 6:30, and left at 7:30. When he returned, his clock showed 4:00. Then his journey took one and one-half hours and the correct time is 9:00.

5 Fiendish Puzzlers

5.1 The Man in the Bar I

The man had hiccups. The barman recognized this from his speech and drew the gun to give the man a shock. It worked and cured the hiccups, so the man was grateful (and no longer needed the water).

5.2 The Man in the Bar II

The man behind the bar was in the process of robbing the place. He had already shot the barman and he shot the man entering the bar to escape and to avoid recognition.

5.3 The Man in the Bar III

It was an iron bar! (*Ouch!*)

5.4 Another Man in a Bar

The guilty man was a Siamese twin, joined at the waist to his brother. The judge could not send the guilty twin to prison without unfairly sentencing the innocent brother.

5.5 The Deadly Block of Wood

The man was a midget who worked in a circus as a star attraction because of his billing as the world's smallest dwarf. Each day, he measured himself with a piece of wood that was exactly his height. One day, a rival dwarf mischievously sawed two inches from the piece of wood. The man mistakenly thought he had grown and would therefore lose his fame and status as the world's smallest dwarf, so he committed suicide.

5.6 The Two Barbers

The traveller deduced, correctly, that since there were only two barbers in the town, each must cut the other's hair. Therefore, the smart barber cut the scruffy barber's hair untidily. The scruffy barber gave the smart barber his tidy haircut. The traveller therefore chose the scruffy barber as the one who would give the best haircut.

5.7 The Mongolian Postal Service

Boris placed the flute diagonally in a suitcase that measured 1 metre by 1 metre. This suitcase was quite acceptable to the postal officials because its sides measured 1 metre. From corner to corner, it measures 1.414 metres— the square root of two.

Incidentally, if his flute had measured 1.7 metres, he could have fitted it across the diagonal of a box whose sides were 1 metre long. The diagonal of a cube is the square root of three times its side—1.73 metres.

From a theoretical mathematical viewpoint, there is no reason why this process cannot be extended indefinitely. If Boris could construct a four dimensional box with 1 metre sides, then he could get a 2 metre flute in it (square root of 4) and a 25 dimensional construction could contain a 5 metre flute while still meeting the rules of having no side longer than 1 metre!

5.8 Heaven

Adam and Eve were the only people there without navels. Because they were not born, they had never had umbilical cords and, therefore, did not have 'belly buttons.'

5.9 Fool's Gold

The easiest solution is to roll both cylinders across the floor. The hollow cylinder will roll farther than the solid one. Its mass is distributed away from its middle, giving it, in terms of physics, a higher moment of inertia than the solid cylinder. Many experiments involving rotating the cylinders would reveal the hollow cylinder, but rolling them is the simplest approach.

5.10 Man in Bar, Again!

The barman's daughter had been murdered by the identical twin of the man who entered the bar. The murderer had been acquitted because of a technicality. (e.g. an illegal search by the police). So the barman longed for revenge. He had seen the murderer in court. He did not know that the murderer had a twin, and, consequently, he shot an innocent man who had entered his bar by chance.

5.11 The Plane Hijacker

The hijacker asked for two parachutes (it is believed) in order to deceive the authorities into thinking that he intended to take a hostage. They therefore gave him two good parachutes. Had he asked for one only, they would have known it was for him and could have given him a dud parachute with a hole in it. By asking for two, he eliminated that risk. Once he knew he had two good parachutes, either would do for his escape.

5.12 Wealth Tax

If there were n inhabitants, and the poorest man owned wealth to the value of $x, then the riches of the citizens in ascending sequence were: $x, 2x, 4x, 8x, 16x, 32x,....2^{n-1}x$.

Thus, when the richest man has given away the sum of all preceding amounts in the sequence, he is left with just $x. He therefore becomes the poorest man and everyone else, having doubled their fortune, moves one place up the ladder. However, the overall distribution of wealth in the country has not changed, only the owners have.

If you want to test this, then try the model with just five citizens owning $1, $2, $4, $8, $16.

5.13 Death on the Train

The man had just completed a course of treatment intended to cure him of blindness. He had high hopes of success. He travelled home on the train with the handkerchief as a blindfold to protect his eyes from the light.

He could not wait and decided to remove the blindfold to test his eyesight. When he removed the blindfold, he could see nothing and assumed that the treatment had failed. He could not face the future as a blind man and, therefore, he stepped out of the speeding train to his death.

The treatment had, in fact, been successful, but he had unfortunately removed the blindfold while the train was in a long tunnel. The carriage was in complete darkness.

5.14 The Amorous Commuter

The Slough trains depart from Maidenhead at five past every hour. The Reading Trains depart at ten past the hour.

If John arrives at any time between ten past the hour and five past the next hour, then the first train to arrive will be bound for Slough. He will catch the Reading train only if he happens to arrive between five past and ten past the hour. It is therefore 11 times more likely that he will catch the Slough train than the Reading train.

5.15 Short Roads

The shortest solution is shown. It represents some 27.3 miles of road in total and therefore saves a precious mile in road-building expense compared to the two diagonals. Someone starting from A would have a shorter journey to D but a longer one to B or C.

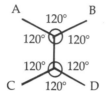

5.16 The Hunter and the Bear

Plainly, the North Pole is one answer to this question. However, it is not the only answer. The other points all lie close to the South Pole.

Any point one mile due north of a circle around the earth with a circumference of exactly one mile will meet the conditions. This circle lies approximately 0.16 miles north of the South Pole.

Starting one mile north of this circle, you could walk one mile south, one mile east (or west), which would take you exactly round the earth to the same point, and then one mile north, which would bring you back to your original starting point.

Similarly, any point one mile due north of a circle of circumference 0.5 miles or 0.25 miles or 0.125 miles etc. would work equally. There are indeed an infinite number of points all less than 1.2 miles from the South Pole that would satisfy the requirements of the problem.

In any event, the bear would still be white, because only polar bears could survive such cold. There are supposed to be no polar bears at the South Pole, but that may be a false assumption!

5.17 The Arm of the Postal Service

The three men had been together on a flying mission in the Pacific. Their plane had come down and they were adrift for many days in a dinghy. They had had some water but no food and were gradually starving to death. Eventually, out of desperation, they agreed to amputate their left arms in order to eat them. They swore a solemn oath that each would have his left arm cut off. One of the three was a doctor and he amputated the arms of one and then later of the other of his colleagues. Just before his turn came, they were rescued. However, his oath was still binding and he later had to have his arm amputated and sent to his colleagues for them to see that the oath had been kept.

5.18 A Weighty Problem I

If the weights can be placed in either of the scale pans, then you can solve the problem with weights of 1, 3, 9, and 27 pounds only. With that combination, any weight from 1 to 40 pounds can be measured.

If the weights can be placed in one scale pan only, then you need the weights 1, 2, 4, 8, 16, and 32 pounds, which enables you to measure any weight up to 63 pounds. This latter solution is really an example of counting with a binary number system where any number can be expressed as the sum of 2 raised to various powers. For example, 63 expressed in binary form is 111111.

5.19 A Weighty Problem II

Let us call the balls A, B, C, D......L. Start by weighing four against four. If they balance, then weigh any of the remaining three against any three of the good balls. If they balance then we know the odd one is the remaining ball and we can identify whether it is heavier or lighter in the final weighing. If the three against three do not balance than we take the three containing the odd ball and weigh any one against another.

If the first weighing of four against four does not produce a balance, then the second weighing involves three against three with balls switched between the two pans and a good ball introduced So:

If $A + B + C + D > E + F + G + H$

We try $A + B + E$ against $C + F + J$

If $A + B + E = C + F + J$ then we know that either D is heavier or G or H is lighter, so we weigh G against H.

If $A + B + E > C + F + J$ then we know that either F is lighter or A or B is heavier, so we weigh A against B.

If $A + B + E < C + F + J$ then we know that either E is lighter or C is heavier, so we weigh either against a good ball: e.g., K against E.

An alternative second weighing is $A + B + E$ against $C + D + F$, which follows similar lines to the above.

ABOUT THE AUTHOR

Paul Sloane was born in Scotland in 1950. He was brought up in the north of England and went to Trinity Hall, Cambridge University, where he took a first-class honors degree in Engineering. While at Cambridge, he met his wife, who is a teacher. They live in Farnborough, England, with their three daughters.

Paul Sloane's career has been mainly in computer sales and marketing. He is now the Managing Director of a personal computer software company. His job involves considerable travel within Europe and the USA. His hobbies include reading, golf, music, and chess. He has always had a keen interest in puzzles and he tries out new problems mercilessly on his daughters. Amazingly, they seem to thrive on it!

INDEX